HOW TO WARRIOR
by Fionna and Cake
A TALE OF DEADLY QUESTS, DARING RESCUES, AND DEFEATING EVIL!

Written by Christopher Hastings

Illustrations by Zachary Sterling

TITAN BOOKS

London

An Insight Editions Book

CONTENTS

INTRODUCTION

Dear Quester of the Near Future,

So you'd like to get some adventuring done in your life. But you have no idea where to start! That's totally understandable. I've met a lot of people who just sit in their house, holding a sword, not sure what to do next.

Conversely, I have met fellow adventurers who have set off with **NO PREPARATION** whatsoever! And then I don't meet them ever again! Because they get zapped by evil wizards and scorched by gnarly dragons!

Or do they get scorched by their own . . . carelessness?

It's hard to blame them. Up until now, no book like this has been written! Except *The Enchiridion*, but like, there's only one copy of that, so it's pretty hard to check out of the library or the deadly ruins of a lost civilization or whatever.

So Cake and I have decided to help out! Because we're pretty nice, dang it! We have set out on a quest to create the best book on what **YOU** should do on a quest.

Now, we're not experts. But we've been around the **TOTALLY INSANE** magical and treacherous block a few times! So through the course of this book, we'll show you all the little tips and tricks we've picked up on how to survive around these parts.

Cool swords? I've got a ton! Exercises and battle techniques? Yo, I do that stuff before I've even completely woken up in the morning! I will show you my best! We'll even let you in on the secrets of **MAKING YOUR OWN DOPE GEAR**!

Once you've completed your training, we'll take you along with us so you can see how we deal with the strange denizens of this supernatural world. You'll be glad you know how to talk to a magical tree when he's got the only apple around and you're lost and starving!

We know some real dumb-dumbs, y'all.

But it's not just the perils of the wilderness! You need to learn to deal with towns, too. Towns are full of people who might just be the folks who end up handing you your quest—or, at the very least, a side quest. They could also be the very foes you need to defeat. People, huh? There sure are several different kinds of them.

After that . . . who knows where we might end up? The center of the multiverse? The deepest pits of the Nightosphere? Probably! It would be weird if we didn't since I just mentioned it! And let's be honest, if you end up in the Nightosphere, you'd better have this tome memorized, or you're gonna end up a demon (or monster) in the Nightosphere.

See you on the next page!

—FIONNA & CAKE

P.S. IF YOU USE THIS KNOWLEDGE FOR EVIL, CAKE WILL CLAW YOUR FACE OFF. THEN I'LL PUNT IT INTO THE NEAREST DUNGEON.

P.P.S. And yes, we'll know if you try! We wrote the book! Author magic!

FIONNA'S SWORDS and CAKE'S TROPHIES

I'll admit, my favorite weapons are usually Madam Right Jab and Lady Left Hook, but sometimes you have to bring a sword to the party!

WISH STAR SWORD

Prince Gumball made this for me! The blade is retractable, so it's like, "Oh, why are you carrying that microphone looking thing, dur dur, I'm a bad guy," and then *SNIKT! STABPRISE!*

CUTE SWORD

Look at his face! He is the **SWEETEST!**

And then when your enemies are all cooin' their minds out, BAM, he gets sharp and mean REAL quick!

LASSO SWORD

Now, you might think, "Fionna, that is just a rope tied to a sword handle." But none of these **OTHER** swords got me out of the well I got pushed in that one time.

SWORD OF THE PHOENIX

If it gets hit too hard, it lights on fire and crumbles apart. But then a little baby sword is rebirthed in the flame!

THE SANDMAN

Forged from the sand of the king of sleep himself, one touch of this fella, and it's good night.

SKATE-BOARD SWORD

Wear a helmet when riding this sword! Also wear an **ENTIRE SUIT** of armor. If you mess up a kick flip on this, it'll lob your flippin' ankles off, bud!

GHOST SWORD

I keep losing it. Is it there right now? I don't know. It's invisible.

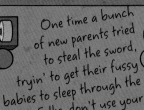

One time a bunch of new parents tried to steal the sword, tryin' to get their fussy babies to sleep through the night. Folks, don't use your sword on a baby.

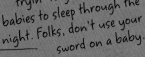

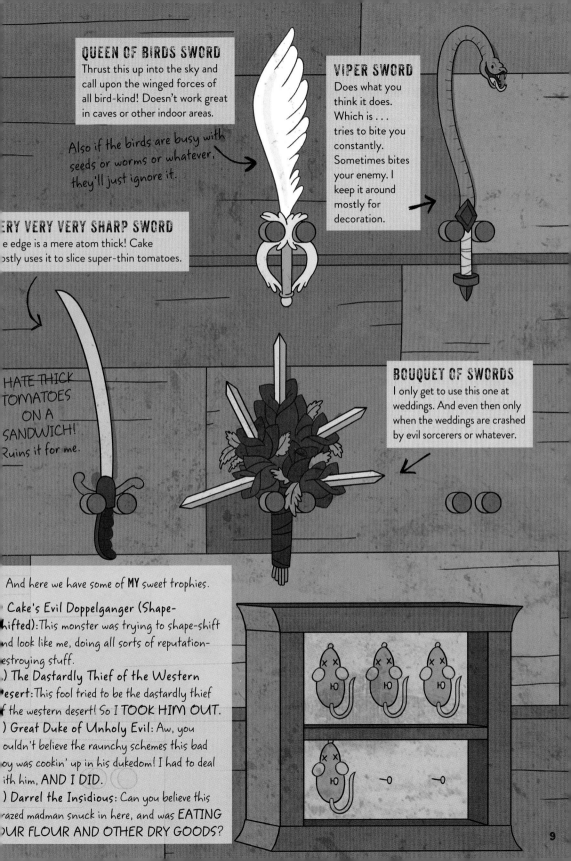

QUEEN OF BIRDS SWORD
Thrust this up into the sky and call upon the winged forces of all bird-kind! Doesn't work great in caves or other indoor areas.

Also if the birds are busy with seeds or worms or whatever, they'll just ignore it.

VIPER SWORD
Does what you think it does. Which is . . . tries to bite you constantly. Sometimes bites your enemy. I keep it around mostly for decoration.

ERY VERY VERY SHARP SWORD
e edge is a mere atom thick! Cake ostly uses it to slice super-thin tomatoes.

HATE THICK TOMATOES ON A SANDWICH! Ruins it for me.

BOUQUET OF SWORDS
I only get to use this one at weddings. And even then only when the weddings are crashed by evil sorcerers or whatever.

And here we have some of **MY** sweet trophies.

Cake's Evil Doppelganger (Shape-hifted): This monster was trying to shape-shift nd look like me, doing all sorts of reputation-estroying stuff.
) The Dastardly Thief of the Western esert: This fool tried to be the dastardly thief f the western desert! So I TOOK HIM OUT.
) Great Duke of Unholy Evil: Aw, you ouldn't believe the raunchy schemes this bad oy was cookin' up in his dukedom! I had to deal ith him, AND I DID.
) Darrel the Insidious: Can you believe this razed madman snuck in here, and was EATING UR FLOUR AND OTHER DRY GOODS?

WARMUPS AND FIGHT MOVES

If you're gonna go out questing, you gotta be ready to deal with **ANYTHING**. That means you need to be ready to fight someone or something at a moment's notice. Here's how we warm up and prepare!

Muscle stretch! Get those muscles loose! Point at stuff that's really far away! Bone stretch!

Mind stretch! Solve a puzzle to get a strong mind and save yourself from brain-busters!

Now that you're stretched and warm and maybe wield psychokinetic powers, let's practice **BATTLE MOVES!**

THREE-KICK SURPRISE:

Start with a standard kick, wherever you deem appropriate on your opponent's body. Then follow up with a **SWEET** jump kick from your other leg! Your opponent will think, "Yikes! These kicks are hurtin' me bad! Good thing Fionna only has two legs, and therefore, only two kicks!" That's when you give him a **PUNCH**! Surprise! The third kick came from your arm!

DAVY JONES WRASSLE:

Should you find yourself doing battle along a water's edge, lock your arms around your opponent's midsection and thrust off the ground, taking him off his feet. Carry your opponent to the water and then dump him in. Works especially well against Paper People, Fire Folk, and generally anyone who isn't waterproof.

THE BONY FIST:

If your opponent is a skeleton, quickly yank his skeleton hand off and then punch him with his own hand! He will be humiliated in front of all his skeleton friends and crumble in embarrassment. All the skeleton friends will also crumble, but out of fear that one of them will be next to suffer this fate.

YOU LOOK TIRED:

Tell your opponent he looks tired. It will **SOUND** sympathetic and caring, but **ACTUALLY** it's a secret diss. He'll get all defensive and self-conscious, and then while he's distracted, you can punch him really hard—or just leave!

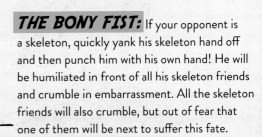

Crafting Your Own Sweet Enchanted Gear

Magical weapons, armor, and accessories. Any survival-minded adventurer needs them! But buying them from a retailer is expensive, and you might get ripped off! That Ring of Good Punching might actually just be a Ring of Okay Punching.

And trying to find the right equipment in piles of dungeon loot takes up too much time! Not to mention how impossible it is to scavenge up all the pieces of a matched set.

But it's easy to make your own equipment for adventuring! Just take normal stuff and enchant it with some of the magic garbage that's literally everywhere in Ooo!

ANTI-PETRIFCATION ARMOR:
A whole bunch of broken mirror shards glued onto a shirt are just the thing for fighting medusas, gorgons, and cockatrices! Let them look at you with their petrifying gaze from any angle, and they'll see their own dumb faces looking back! Then BAM! Who's the statue now? It is them. They are the statue.

CLIMBING AND ALSO GRABBING GLOVES:
These gloves are made from Prince Gumball's stickiest experimental mega-taffy. They're great for tough climbs or for grabbing something you NEVER want to un-grab. Don't clap while wearing the grabbing gloves.

FIRE KINGDOM SURVIVAL GOWN:
The Fire Kingdom is hot. **CRAZY** hot. Ideally, we could get a personal cooling spell from the Ice Queen, but she's ba-nonkers and won't share **ANYTHING**. So rig up some fans and stick them on the ball gown!

TRANSLATOR HELMET:
Old Gilbert **SAYS** he's the oldest tree alive, with roots that spread deep and far across the entire world. Whether he's full of it or not, Gilbert's definitely the only **MULTILINGUAL** tree I know! Stick an old horn in the ear hole of a helmet, and stuff some of Gilbert's leaves in there. When someone speaks a language you don't know, it gets filtered through Gilbert's magical knowing leaves, and when it reaches your ears, you can understand it!

SLIME BOMBS:
Toss these behind you to totally slip up pesky pursuers you're fleeing. We got a lot of slime in the house, and we had to do something with it. It was a gift from the Slime Prince. I think it was meant for eating but . . . no way. Gross.

CAPE OF ROC FEATHERS:
Hold out the cape when you're falling a great distance, and this feather cape will help you float down safely!

COOL LEVITATION SNEAKS:
Witches are throwing out old flying brooms all the time! Usually there's still a little good magic in the bristles. Stick them in your shoes and you can float around! Good for stealth missions. GREAT for avoiding stepping on dog poop.

GET WILD WITH
Stretchy
POWERS!

Magic swords and sneakers are real nice . . . if you need them! But I've got stretchy magic, and therefore am SO POWERFUL I DON'T NEED ANY OF THAT JUNK! Check THESE out!

← Alright, first up, I can be A GIANT CAT! HA HA HA, COWER BEFORE ME, Y'ALL!

↑ OR A TINY CAT! BAM!

THAT'S PRETTY COOL, B* I THINK WE'RE TRYIN TO BE A BIT MORE CREATIVE THAN THAT.

Alright, alright, chec this out. Stretch ou: to coat the walls, floor, and ceiling of a room . . . BOOM! Instant Cake Trap!

Sometimes, TO BE NICE, I turn into a weapon for Fionna, but I don't like it! It doesn't feel nice to be swung against some crocodile monster's face or some such! →

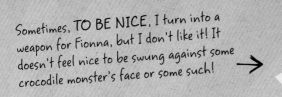

SORRY . . . HOW ABOUT A VEHICLE?

I hope you don't think I'm turning into a boat! I DO NOT GET WET. No cars either! Functional wheels are impossible! Here, check this out. LOOOONG CAT.

You can ride on a long cat, or a big cat. And if you want something else, the answer is . . .

A Tale from the Monochromicorn-Cat Wars
by Cake

Years ago, the cats and the Mo-chros battled HECKA FIERCELY for dominion over the crystal dimension. But there was no battle fiercer than the one for Crystal Rock, the spire on the edge of the crystal plains! That is because it had a breathtaking view of the crystal ocean. Good real estate, feel me? Both sides were so worn out from fighting that they were fighting for some decent vacation space!

The battle was going CRAZY. Bombs were dropping! Lasers were firing! Cats were clawing, and Mo-chros were flying around and making black holes and whatnot. The battle ended with the entire crystal beach community buried in rubble. One brave cat soldier barely escaped with his life but was now trapped in a small crystal house, unable to get out because of the debris. And there was a MONOCHROMICORN in there with him!

Oh yeah, you better believe they fought! The cat was all, "I claim this house for the Cat Nation!" and the Mo-chro was like, "Tap tap tap, hold on, I'm tapping out Morse code with my feet," but she was pretty hostile about it. They battled for hours, holding on to whatever tiny piece of territory they could get in that house. They eventually came to a stalemate and decided to wait for whichever side could dig them out first. The crystal person who lived in the house was happy that they stopped trashing it.

After a while, they got to talking. As it turned out, neither of them really LIKED being at war. The cat told stories of his home, filled with leather couches to scratch up ALL day long. The Mo-chro tapped her hoof for a while, eventually getting around to mentioning some field she liked to hang out at. And they kept on chattin' throughout the night.

In the morning, cat rescuers were able to break through into the house. But when they got there, neither the cat nor the Monochromicorn was there. You know why? Because they fell in love and found a way out, working together, and ran off in the night to live a life of smoochin' in the countryside! WOOO! That is the good stuff.

FLORA AND FAUNA, FRIEND OR FOE?

We've stretched. We're armed. We're finally ready to face the **HECKA DANGEROUS OUTDOORS!** Getting out of your house is a pretty vital Quest Move. If you're spending any extended period of time in the forest, you should know some ins and outs about the stuff you'll find in the wild.

ROAMING PIÑATAS: SEEK OUT.

If you're in danger of going too long without candy, you can track a wild piñata and harvest it for its candy. Just be nice and put him back together again when you've eaten enough!

SKULL FLAME MOTHS:

AVOID. They are on fire, and they will light you on fire too! It's a no-brainer.

A FISH THAT CLAIMS TO BE YOUR MOTHER:

AVOID. The hauntingly kind voice bubbling out from that pond isn't really your mother! It's a weird enchanted fish! How many people does that fish trick with that one? Yikes.

HUG ROCKS: DEPENDS.

If they're too big or kind of overzealous, the hug rocks can go from cute to crush really fast. But if you lie down in the rain, they cluster around you to make a nice shelter!

MUSHROOMS:

SEEK OUT. Mushrooms are evidence of mushroom pizzas growing just under the soil's surface! **NICE, DUDE.**

BOOK TREES: SEEK OUT. Another type of vaguely cognizant magic tree. They found out that paper is made from trees, and then they found out all the stuff made from paper. They're so desperate not to be turned into toilet paper that they just straight up grow fully written novels. Sometimes they're good! But most of the time they're about someone who is stuck in one place for a really, really long time. You write what you know.

SPLODOPINES: AVOID. These little spiny creatures explode into a shower of needles if they get scared. And they WILL get scared, no matter what you do. Might as well take cover and yell, "BOO!"

CACTUS IN THE WOODS: AVOID. Why's that cactus in the woods?! Aah! It's a trap! What kind of trap?! Who cares!

CLOWN BUSH: AVOID. No. Just no. Creepy-looking bush, stop looking like a clown! It's weird!

INVISIBLE LIONS: AVOID. Oh boy, if you think one's nearby, just start throwing flour around. If you suddenly see a vaguely lion-shaped white dust cloud, **GET OUT OF THERE.**

SENTIENT TREES: SEEK OUT. These trees have been stuck in one place for a **REALLY** long time! They desperately crave gossip. Tell them the good stuff, and they'll give you some fruit!

WHEN NOT TO FIGHT THE MONSTER

When the monster is like . . . a dragon that could eat a country! Actually, we just figured out how to keep this guy from getting cranky. We tell him stories! And then he gets sleepy and just hibernates for a long time.

CAKE: You're welcome, potential countries that could get gobbled!

FIONNA: Hey, big guy! You ready for a nice story? Let's see, this one is called the, uh . . . **"THE DRAGON WHO SAVED EVERYONE AND IS GREAT."**

FIONNA: So, in a totally distant land, there lived a dragon. His name was Dragonio.

CAKE: Nice.

FIONNA: He wasn't a very big dragon, but he was happy doing his work, eating rocks—

CAKE: Do dragons eat rocks?

FIONNA: This one does! **SHUSH**. . . . He was eating rocks for a local monster mining company that was tunneling out caves to fill with hoards of treasure. It was a peaceful life for the dragon! Until one day Fiercebreath flew through the dragon's town. Fiercebreath was the mightiest—

CAKE: Girl, your details are wobblier than a rickety bridge!

FIONNA: UGH. Well, you take over then!

CAKE: Now we're talkin'! Fiercebreath was a **FINE**-lookin' big ole dragon man! **HUGE** muscles! Gorgeous teeth! And big wings! **STRONG** wings. That Fiercebreath could fly to **SPACE** if he felt like it.

FIONNA: Don't forget, this is supposed be about Dragonio.

CAKE: Oh, right. So, uh, Fiercebreath was like, "Hey everybody! There's a real **NASTY** kingdom of **HUMANS** a few towns over—"

FIONNA: Hey! I'M human!

CAKE: It's just a story, baby. Anyway, Fiercebreath was like, "Those nasty humans are building a town that is **FAR** too big for my liking, and I have a feeling they're going to be sending some rude knights our way to pillage our treasure caves! Who's gonna help me fight them?" Well, you'd think the supposed hero of this story, Dragonio, would, but no. He was a dumb little baby of a dragon and—

FIONNA: Cake, he was just accustomed to his quiet, rustic life, eating rocks.

CAKE: Whatever! I say he was a coward! And he said, "Oh no, chomp chomp chomp. Let me stick to these delicious rocks! I guess I like them?" And the **BEAUTIFUL** Fiercebreath was nearly reduced to tears, and he was like, "Fine, I'll go blast those humans with my fire breath all by myself."

MARSHALL LEE: Hey, Fionna. Hey, Cake. Are you two telling the story of "The Dragon Who Saved Everyone and Is Great"?

FIONNA: Marshall Lee! What are you doing here?! We're trying to keep this dragon asleep with this story! And don't act like you know the story! We're making it up as we go along!

MARSHALL LEE: Ha ha, I **LOVE** the story of Dragonio. Here, I'll jump in. Fiercebreath attacked the human city! He rained so much fire down on their roofs! It was crazy—and rad. But the evil human king, uh . . . **KING BAD BUTT** said, "Yo, this dragon is doing cool stuff with that fire, and I hate it. **CAPTURE HIM.**"

FIONNA: Oh jeez, please don't upset the dragon we're telling the story to . . .

MARSHALL LEE: Chill, Fionna! I'm just making it exciting. With Fiercebreath held captive, King Bad Butt was emboldened to expand his empire, because he thought dragons were actually pretty weaktacular. So pretty soon, human armies were marching into

Dragonio's little town, very much enjoying all the lovely gold and treasure chests stored up in their dragon caves.

CAKE: Seriously, boy, you're gonna get this real-life dragon mad for real if you keep saying stuff like that.

MARSHALL LEE: Whatever, I'm bored with this story anyway. See you later. Vampire kisses and Nightosphere wishes . . .

FIONNA: Agh, he is so frustrating! Okay! So Dragonio flipped out and started flapping his wings really hard! With a strength he didn't even know he had! And he caused a huge and powerful wind to blow away all the human soldiers!

CAKE: Ha ha, **YES**! They were spinning and flying around, and they all landed right in a volcano!

FIONNA: Seriously?

CAKE: Why not? Yeah! They landed in a volcano, and the magma burned them all up, and Dragonio laughed at them, because he was a fire dragon and that would **NEVER** happen to him!

FIONNA: Anyway, little Dragonio realized he might be stronger and more able than he gave himself credit for, and he knew it was up to him to save his hero, Fiercebreath, and defeat the evil King Bad Butt, whose name is actually growing on me. It's a good villain name. You know where you stand with a King Bad Butt.

CAKE: Yeah, right. You just like it because **MAAARSHALL** made it up.

FIONNA: No, I don't! Stop it! Uh, so Dragonio flew near the human city, then landed in a nearby swamp and waited until nightfall. He knew the people would

capture him just like they captured Fiercebreath, so he decided to go in **STEALTH STYLE**. He tucked up his dragon wings and crept his way through the dark city side streets and back alleys—

CAKE: And nobody noticed the *WAM WAM WAM* of his big, giant feet tip-toein' around?

FIONNA: We already said he's not that big! It's plausible! Anyway, he . . .

LUMPY SPACE PRINCE: Fionna and cat! Why, whatever are you doing by this sleepy dragon!? **HELLO, DRAGON, HOW DO YOU D—**

FIONNA: LSP! *SHH!* We're telling him a story to keep him from getting up and burning all of Ooo to the ground.

LUMPY SPACE PRINCE: Oh, is **THAT** what that was? I hope you don't mind. I have some notes.

FIONNA: What?

LUMPY SPACE PRINCE: Here, this will fix it. Fiercebreath was not a warrior, but a **BEAUTIFUL** dragon princess that Dragonio had to rescue.

FIONNA: What?! No way! Fiercebreath was a powerful warrior, and this is about Dragonio learning his own strength in the face of that!

LUMPY SPACE PRINCE: Fine, Dragonio is a beautiful dragon princess.

FIONNA: LSP, NO.

LUMPY SPACE PRINCE: Hmm . . . you're not very open to critique. You won't make it very far that way. Very well. But let me have a try at continuing the story.

FIONNA: Just don't jonk it up.

LUMPY SPACE PRINCE Dragonio crept his way through the city and made it to the castle, under which his hero, Fiercebreath, was held by the vicious, awful humans. They made him mop their floors! And do their dishes! It was terrible. Dragonio was terribly moved by such a sight, and his rage could not be contained! With a great thrash of his scaly tail, he struck down the castle wall! The castle shook, and the humans didn't know **WHAT** to do!

FIONNA: Okay, you're actually doing alright with this.

LUMPY SPACE PRINCE: And that is when the **BEAUTIFUL HUMAN PRINCESS** . . .

FIONNA: Never mind.

LUMPY SPACE PRINCE:
. . . emerged from her tower. "Wait! Dragon! Do not destroy us!"
"Why shouldn't I?" responded Dragonio.
"Because," responded the princess. "I love you!"
Dragonio was astonished. He was not of royal blood. He was just a lowly rock-eater. How could a princess love him?
"As a friend!" she clarified.
"Oh, well that's well and proper, in that case," he thought.

CAKE: You got some weird ideas about **EVERYTHING**, lump man.

LUMPY SPACE PRINCE: The platonic friendship of the princess made Dragonio spare the human castle, with its human butt king. But he swore if humankind were to ever try stealing the treasure of the dragons again, they'd only be able to enjoy that treasure as totally burnt-up skeletons, if you catch my meaning.

FIONNA: Great! Okay, you're all done. Let's finish this up before the dragon gets mad at being told a story without a consistent narrative voice. Dragonio freed Fiercebreath, and they left for their dragon home! Dragonio was hailed a hero, and sometimes the human princess comes to visit, and they play basketball. The End.

CAKE: Pretty abrupt ending, girl.

FIONNA: I'm getting hungry! Let's go into town and get some **FOOD IN OUR FACES! YEAH!**

CAKE: I refuse to argue with that!

CEMETERY FOR THE AWESOME FALLEN

Normally I'd think boneyards would be spooked out to the max, but I like this one! It's former heroes of the realm and stuff! Take some time to honor the questers who have quested before you!

1 DEB THE TERRIBLE: When an asteroid fell to Ooo and a weird monster came out of it, she threw it into the ocean! She helped kids with their homework! Why did she have this name? Honestly we all really liked her.

2 WARRIOR QUEEN CASHEW OF NUTS: This lady basically took over an entire continent and single-handedly planted all the Nut People. And while they were growing all cozy in the dirt, she fought off crows that tried to eat them!

3 BILLIE! She fought a bear!

4 PRINCE HYSTERICAL IV: The magnificent clown prince of the Chuckle Kingdom. Battled an invading kingdom with nothing but pie catapults. It was incredible. The Chuckle Kingdom was successfully invaded and destroyed, but still . . . pretty funny.

5 SPOOKEMS THE WIZARD: There was only one skeleton this powerful necromancer couldn't bring back to life: his own.

6 LESLIE OF A THOUSAND ARROWS: Oh boy, Leslie hated this name. She actually shot way more than a thousand arrows. But she arrowed up a lot of bad folks, and we'll always remember her for it, even if we can't remember exactly how many there were after a thousand-ish.

7 JENNIFER OF THE DEEP: A merperson hero of all underwater creatures! Not sure how she ended up in this land-based dirt cemetery.

8 GHOST PRINCE: He's technically the ruler of this cemetery, though he hasn't done much for it! Look how spooky it is! Get it together, Ghost Prince. This place is a mess.

I can still see like a billion ghosts, girl. CATVISION!

I THINK I'M KINDA GLAD I DON'T HAVE THAT RIGHT NOW.

Yeah, you should be!

THE BAZAAR OF THE BIZARRE

Ah, the weird giant market! It's like a mall but outdoors, and usually there's some shadowy figure beckoning you to a forbidden stall of evil magic. We do most of our shopping here.

CAR...
V...

WOVEN GOODS

Custom red carpet to fill your whole home! Be a star wherever you are! Even in the potty.

POSSIBLY TRUE HISTORICAL TAPESTRIES

BUCKET FULL O' RUGS

CHEESE AND HONEY

BEEF HONEY

TALKING CHEESE

FROG'S CHEESE

CRUMBL... SON OF CH...

FRUITS AND VEGETABLES

Righteous Bananas

Evil Bananas

Okay Bananas

Chocolate-Flavored Tomatoes
Thousand-Year-Old Kale
Brussel Sprouts with Prizes Inside
Leaves
Cherry Peppers
Sergeant Peppers
Actual Gold Potatoes

Ice Sculptures
Beautify your lawn with ice sculptures! Guaranteed to impress until about noon.

CANDY

WARS
DOOR

REAL ESTATE
*Buy shares of the moon!
Own land at the bottom of
the fast-developing ocean!*

*A home in another dimension takes up
less space yet has more room!*

Beauty Supplies

Treasured
Memory-Scented
Body Wash

Fairy Spit

PETS

Cloning of
deceased pets
available!

WIZARD STAFFS

Chill Staff:
For relaxing

Staff
of Soda
Drinking

PPY BIRTHDAY
GING CHICKEN

FRIENDLY
TOOTHLESS
GOAT

Staff
of
Magic
Missile

FLAME
HOG

CUDDLE BOT

Staff of
Spider
Dominion
(Warning: Will
make gross
spiders be
your friend)

Staff of
Rainbow Spray:
(Not for use
indoors)

Staff
of Dirt
Removal

Thing on a String

Tall Pole

Slightly
Smaller
Cardboard
Box

CAT
SUPPLIES

Medium-Sized
Cardboard Box

MEATS

Don't Tell the
Wyverns What
We're Doing Here
Wyvern Leg

Antibiotic-
Free Minotaur
Brisket

Free-Range
Robot Bits

Wyvern
Belly

Swap Swan's
Greeting Cards!

You'll be a die-hard for my nice cards! Take a look,
you'll be hooked! Birthday, wedding, or funeral,
you won't find a greeting as beautiful!

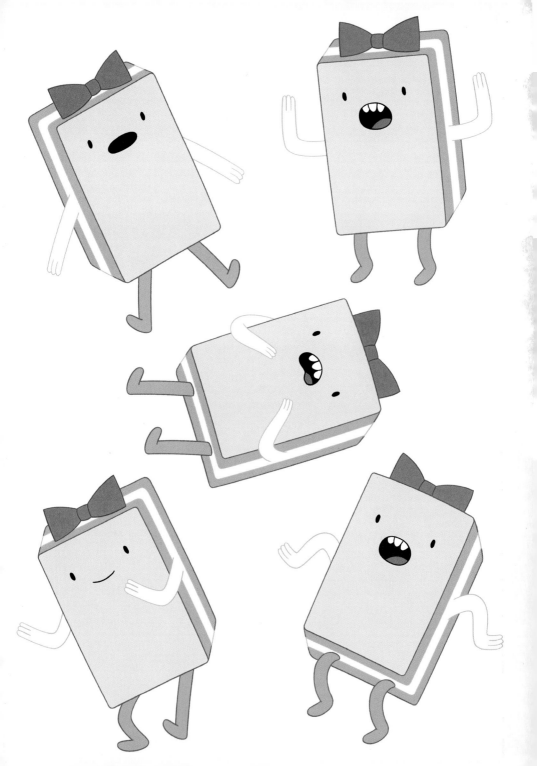

May you always
remember which one
of you came first.

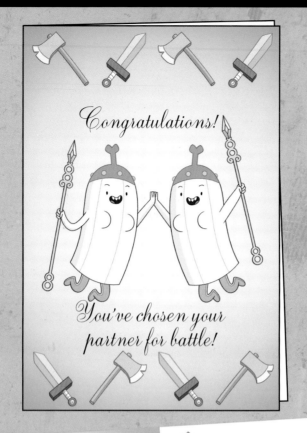

Congratulations!

You've chosen your partner for battle!

Your journey begins with a giant cake! May gifts of fine china help you on your journey.

I SAW YOUR EX YESTERDAY.

I SAID THEY LOOKED GOOD.

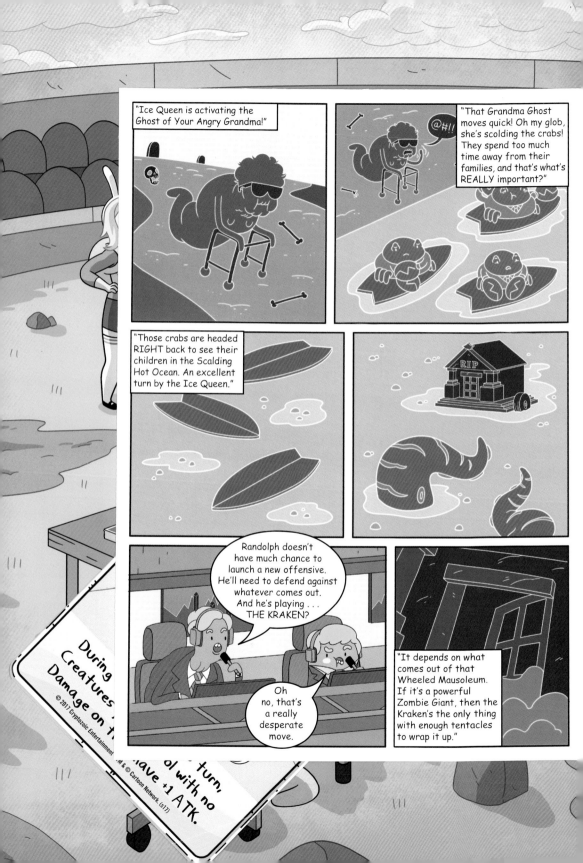

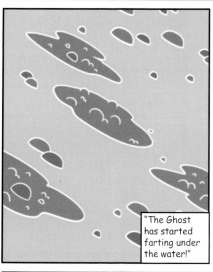

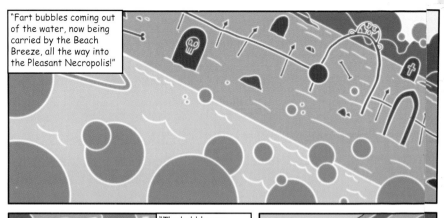

"Fart bubbles coming out of the water, now being carried by the Beach Breeze, all the way into the Pleasant Necropolis!"

"The bubbles are popping! The gas escaping! Oh no, the people of the Necropolis can't take it. They're all falling under the terrible fog of Ghost farts."

"That's it for Ice Queen. Randolph's got this game in the bag."

"Oh, Ice Queen has begun to rain actual ice lightning on everyone around us. Take cover, everyone, good-bye!"

THE CARD WARS
TOURNAMENT

Yo, ABD's not actually that powerful a wizard, though, is she?

ABRACADANIELLE'S MAGIC LESSONS

Citizens of Ooo! I, Abracadanielle, your mightiest spellcaster of the highest level, have decided to bequeath my knowledge of the arcane unto you lowly amateurs. It is my duty to stoke the flames of magic in young students so that it may never die. And, of course, the registration fee is **VERY** reasonable. Here . . . This ritual shall prove to friend and enemy alike that you are a **MIND MAGE** of **IMMENSE PSYCHIC ABILITY**.

In a friendly and jovial setting, propose to an onlooker (whom I shall now call your victim) that you can **SEE INTO THE FUTURE** to predict choices they themselves do not even know yet! And you will demonstrate this with three ordinary items!

Choose three different everyday items around you. For the purposes of this lesson, we'll say a Pen, a Cup, and a Coin. Once you have the objects set in front of you, tell your victim you are going to jot out a note. Choose one of the items, and write it down on a little piece of paper. **MAKE SURE THE VICTIM DOES NOT SEE WHAT YOU WROTE!** Fold up the paper and tuck it away, or hand it to a volunteer, making sure your victim knows that there will be no tampering with the paper at this point. In this example, we'll say you've written down "the Coin."

Now, ask your victim to look upon the three items and take two of them for herself. If the victim has taken the Pen and the Cup, you should make a very big deal of this. "**WHOA!**," "Very interesting!," etc. Then, with much theatricality, you retrieve the paper, and hand it to your victim to read. As she opens it, you boldly proclaim, "I **KNEW** you would leave me the Coin!" They will be amazed.

Now suppose they took the Pen and the Coin instead, leaving the Cup. Well, this spell will still work! It's all in how you sell it! Quickly discard the Cup, and pretend that this is all going exactly as you thought it might, zeroing in on the two items your victim now has. "Oh my, this strange witchcraft amazes me still, even as it unfolds in front of me just as I knew it would! Now, I want you to choose very carefully. . . . Give me one of those items."

If they hand you the Coin, excellent. Act like this was the plan all along. Retrieve the paper and say something like, "Well, well, well, of all these objects, fate has made you decide to give me . . . **THE COIN**." Then hand over the piece of paper and let them read what you wrote on it.

But should they hand you the Pen and keep the Coin—well, this was also your plan all along. Put the Pen aside with the Cup. It is of no consequence. Retrieve the paper, give it to your soon to be astonished victim, and declare, "I have given you three items, and I knew that in the end you would be left with **THE COIN!**"

AND THAT IS MY MOST POWERFUL SPELL! I PASS IT ON TO YOU!

Never do it twice for the same person or in the presence of those who have already witnessed the trick—er, magic spell. **RETAIN YOUR AIR OF MYSTERY!**

SEEMS LIKE MORE OF A . . . TRICK.

COIN

THE GREAT PRINCE GUMBALL'S

Fully Autocratic Mostly Automatic

CANDY CITIZEN CREATOR

Anyone who has tried to make their own candy knows the great effort it demands—
not to mention the skill and luck. Double boilers, caramel thermometers . . . It's
enough to make you lie on a nearby couch for hours! The hassles of creating Living
Candy truly were sent from one of the nine hells to bedevil the good souls of Ooo.
Begone, hassles! Prince Gumball has devised A BETTER WAY!

Come visit this patented machine, and witness
the creation of a Candy Kingdom citizen
yourself! You might even get to pick out what
kind of hat it wears! Wouldn't that be keen?

NOT RECOMMENDED FOR THOSE WHO WOULD QUESTION THE ETHICS OF MECHANIZED EASY LIFE CREATION.

CANDY CITIZEN CREATOR

BY PRINCE GUMBALL

Ah! Fionna! Cake! Welcome to my lab! I was just in the middle of whipping up some new Candy Kingdom citizens! I know what you're thinking—don't I have enough candy citizens? Why do I need to make more?

Well, sometimes you just have to! Did a school bus full of candy accidentally go on a field trip to a pit of monsters? It might have! Anyway, let's see what we've got here.

We'll need to choose the candy species, some type of station or personality, and wrap it all up in a real hot bod!

ADVICE
BY PARTY GODDESS

ARROOOO! Hey everybody! Party Goddess here! Ready to solve all of your puny problems! What you got, ladies?!

Hmm . . . What you got here, Gumball?

Well, I have a state ball later today, and I wanted to see if the Party Goddess had any tips!

Q

Dear Party Goddess,

My best friend recently had a baby. I'm super happy for her, but there's just one thing. I told her years ago the perfect name I wanted to give my baby once I have one. And my friend has stolen the name! Her baby has my someday baby's dream name! Do I confront her on this?

Signed,
Robbed of Name

A Dear R.O.N.,

WOOF, that is a rude situation! On one hand, your friend absolutely broke your trust by taking a special hope for your future, represented by the perfect name for your baby. On the other hand, who cares? It's just a name. It's not like your friend actually **STOLE** your baby!

Here's what I think you need to do. Celebrate the fact that one day when you have a child, you are **FREE** from the shackles of your previously chosen name! You may decide from the **INFINITY OF OTHER OPTIONS** before you! I suggest getting all your friends to come over for a baby-naming party! Everyone can put suggestions in a bowl, and you can dance and shower them all over each other, under a dazzling array of lights, thrumming to the beats of a totally sick groove! Become hypnotized by the rhythm! Fall into a rapture of dance and sound and the rain of thousands of slips of paper with baby names on them! When you finally awaken from your trance, you'll be holding the single slip with the perfect new name for your baby.

And if you don't like it, just go with Drew. It works for boys or girls.

Dear Party Goddess,

I'm in love with a wonderful man. He's from a totally different kingdom, and his foreign ways are mysterious and sexy. There's just one thing that's bothering me. He claims he's actually the heir to the throne of that foreign kingdom . . . but I think he might just be a charming hobo who lives in the woods. Do I just go with it? Or do I challenge him on his claims to princedom?

Signed,

Boyfriend a Prince?

Dear B.A.P.,

I haven't heard of too many princes of faraway kingdoms who actually live alone in the woods, so . . . I'm gonna say it sounds like you're dating Lumpy Space Prince. Nice job preserving the anonymity there! The good news is that it doesn't matter, because LSP is too proud to care. Also I don't know if he can read.

As the Goddess of All Parties, I have dominion over any land that should host a party. And I will tell you that I have traveled between the planes to visit the other-dimensional Lumpy Space, and have experienced their parties. Which is a long way of saying, yes, I have seen that Lumpy Space Prince really is the Prince of Lumpy Space. But he's also not getting un-exiled anytime soon! What I think you should do is give in to his forest-dwelling ways. Invite all the creatures of the forest to a giant bonfire! Set up a DJ so you can have some dope beats and songs! Groove with the forest animals! Under the sway of the music in the unobstructed moonlight, you will come to understand their untamed ways! You'll see your boyfriend funk under the stars, and you will love him even more! You have partied your way into being a FOR-REAL PARTY ANIMAL! With other party animals!

And, in the morning, if you think it's gross and dirty, you can just dump LSP. Because he **IS** gross and dirty.

Dear Party Goddess,

I hang around with a lot of pretty fun friends, but any time there's a party they have a tendency to go overboard. My birthday is coming up, and I want to have a party, but I'm afraid my friends will go too crazy. What do I do?

Signed,

Dreading a Raunchy Party

Dear D.A.R.P.,

Friends who have the tendency to go overboard can be a terrible source of anxiety. Next time you see them, why don't you sit them down and respectfully—
JUST KIDDING! YOU SHOULD THROW A PARTY! YOUR FRIENDS AREN'T THE PROBLEM! YOU'RE THE PROBLEM! LET YOURSELF GO CRAZY! THROW THE PARTY! THROW A MILLION PARTIES! THE PARTY IS THE WAY! THE PARTY IS THE LIFE! SICK BEATS! COOL FOOD! CRAZY FRIENDS! RIDE A BULL! THROW THE PARTY! INVITE SOME BATS! FLY AROUND WITH THE BATS! PARTYYYYYYYY! And then in the morning you can PARTY AGAIN! PARTY PARTY PARTY!

That probably won't b
necessary. But thank
you, Fionna.

TELL ME IF YOU
WANT ME TO
HIT SOMEONE!

Prince Gumball's Gum Ball

Now, at functions like this, you have to keep an eye out for all the subtle political maneuvering that's happening. Everyone is polite, but they're all playing games of secrets and power.

Take a look over there—the Hot Dog Prince and the Pizza Prince look awfully friendly. Hot dogs and pizzas are typically on the opposite sides of a confrontation, but I believe they are making an alliance to seize control of the Midnight Snack Kingdom. And yet both foods are excellent choices for ANY time. Would focusing on the Midnight Snack domain open them up for attack from the Brunch Kingdom? Pizza being folded into brunch options could be very titillating indeed. . . .

And this is interesting—the Slime Prince normally tears it up on the dance floor, but right now he's barely moving at all. I believe that is because that's actually a slime duplicate of the prince. He knows how difficult it is for us non–Slime People to distinguish sentient slime from nonsentient slime. The only question is, is the prince not here because he would find the party boring? I believe he may be elsewhere, using this party as an alibi. In fact, it's likely he's pouring slime into the hood of the Desert Prince's limousine. Slime and sand are natural enemies.

Oh, what's that over there? The Ghost Prince has made a new friend in the Duchess of Screwclank! But are his intensions noble? Everyone knows that the Ghost Prince misses his corporeal body, though he has been parted from it for centuries now. I guess being unable to touch or lift **ANYTHING** doesn't get any easier. Perhaps he will try to get Duchess Screwclank to build him a new steam–powered mecha body? Or does he want to simply possess the metal body of Screwclank herself? Thus granting him not only a new powerful metal body, but the whole Screwclank realm as well!

Oh no . . . and there's the self-proclaimed "One True Queen of Ooo." I can absolutely assure you that she is up to trouble. How'd she even get in here?!

PUNCH! PUNCH!
PUNCH! PUNCH!   *Please don't.*

Everyone stop dancing! Stop drinking small drinks! You need to know the truth! I have gathered it for you because I am a good person!

Don't look at me with accusing eyes! Your accusations are garbage! Dump them in the ocean! Read my newspaper! READ IIIIIIIIT!

Countess Lemongrab's
ACCEPTABLE INFORMER

PRINCE GUMBALL: WEARING PINK SWEATPANTS OUTDOORS? JUST LIKE US?! HE IS ROYALTY! UNACCEPTABLE!

Multiple sources have confirmed that Prince Gumball of the Candy Kingdom was spotted outside his private chambers wearing **PINK SWEATPANTS**. This is **HIGHLY UNACCEPTABLE!** Sweatpants are made of loose-fitting, thick, woven cotton and are attached to the body with elastic bands. Members of **ANY** royal court should only bind their trousers with hard and terrible belts. They should poke your bellies when you sit! And yet the Prince has decided to spit on tradition and take wild kicks at public opinion! **HE WORE THE SWEATPANTS OUTSIDE!** Countess Lemongrab understands that within the private palace halls, there may be shameful secrets and hidden awful doings. If the Prince were to wear the sweatpants while **COMPLETELY ALONE** and only in a special and tiny comfort room . . . This would be **BORDERING** on acceptable. But instead the Prince has decided to throw away his royal station, and that is why the countess must become the queen of the Candy Kingdom! It is the only way! Join my armies! **JOIN THEM!**

SECRET OF THE PRINCE OF COATS: HE IS JUST A BUNCH OF COATS ON A RACK! HE DOES NOT LIVE AS WE DOOOOOOO! WHO MADE HIM A PRIIIIIIIINCE?!

TAIL TUFTS DOESN'T EVEN FRESH-PRESS HIS OWN APPLE JUICE? JUST BUYS IT AT THE MARKET? HE'S FAMOUS FOR LOVING APPLES! THIS IS A HUGE SCANDAAAAAAAL

Tail Tufts was recently spotted headed to the local market by none other than the editor in chief of this very publication. Yes! I, the Countess Lemongrab saw Tail Tufts leave his house when I was nearby for reasons that are **NOT** up for public discussion! **HOW DARE YOU ASK WHY I WAS NEAR TAIL TUFTS' HOME?** Tail Tufts was overheard saying, "Oh goodness, all the luscious apples in the   trees near my home appear to have been stolen and . . . What's that? Countess Lemongrab? What are you doin' behind that tree? And why are you surrounded by apple cores?" My response to Tail Tufts is not of any consequence to this story, **AND NEITHER ARE THE SUPPOSED APPLE CORES REFERENCED IN TAIL TUFTS' QUOTE!** Tail Tufts left his home in a suspicious manner, so I followed him to the market. There I saw him purchase **TWO CONTAINERS OF APPLE JUICE!** I began to shriek in outrage. Tail Tufts responded, "Lemongrab, I understand you're tryin' to trap me in some kinda scandal, but this is a very nice brand of apple juice. And I do love apple juice." **THAT IS IMPOSSIBLE.** Everyone knows that nothing you buy can ever be as good as anything you make! And Tail Tufts loves apple things! His buying apple things after his apples mysteriously vanished is actually proof he does not care about apple things. **THERE.** That is the final word on the subject.

ICE QUEEN'S SECRET MARRIAGE TO TINY PRINCE. NO ONE CAN KNOW IF HE WAS ACTUALLY THERE BECAUSE HE IS TOO TINY TO SEE! VERY FRUSTRATTIIIIING!

HUGE BLOWOUT! FLAME PRINCE GETS MAD AND YELLS AT THE SKY WHEN IT RAINS. HE SHOULD KNOW BETTER THAN TO YELL AT CLOUDS! OOO!

Fionna, this party is donked out. Wanna bail?

HA HA HA . . . WHAAAAAT?

IS IT OR ISN'T IT A DATE?

 OH GOSH, PRINCE GUMBALL JUST ASKED IF I WANTED TO GET OUT OF THE PARTY? IS IT A DATE? GAH, I DON'T KNOW WITH THESE GUYS!

 Girl, you just gotta break it down. These boys can't be that hard to understand!

 OKAY, SO THESE DUDES I HANG WITH ARE COOL, BUT I THINK THEY HAVE NO IDEA HOW TO ACT, LIKE . . . ARE THEY BUDDIES? OR ARE THEY MORE? ON YOUR JOURNEY, YOU MIGHT ENCOUNTER OTHER BOYS WHO LACK THE SAME AWARENESS OF THEIR ACTIONS, AND YOU'LL WANT TO DECIPHER THEIR DEAL.

Did he buy you dinner?

A Uh, kind of? He had me come over to kill a bunch of out-of-control ice cream yetis, and then we ate the ice cream when we were done.

B He just ate molten rocks. . . . I didn't really want any.

C I thought he was going to, but then he turned into a bat and flew away! He thought it was funny!

D No, Lumpy Space Prince will always make you pay for food.

Did he send you meaningful looks?

A His eyes **CONSTANTLY SPARKLE**. I can never tell.

B Any time I looked at him too directly, he'd get shy and accidentally set a tree on fire.

C Marshall would look into my eyes and I thought something was happening, and then I realized he was just trying to vampire-hypnotize me into stealing a firetruck for him to suck the red out of!

D His eyes got really big, with super-defined irises . . . and then he told me my clothes were dirty.

Did he get close to you? Did you hold hands?

A We danced for a while! But it was because he was testing shock-absorbing floor panels that convert footsteps into electricity. . . .

B I accidentally spilled some water on him, and he shrieked and ran away.

C He turned into a magical vampiric mist, and I might have breathed some in.

D No, he kept saying he was royalty and I was common, and I might accidentally "get common on him."

Jeez, okay, maybe they are hard to understand. I don't know; were they at least **NICE** to you?

A He laughed at something I said even though I didn't think it was that funny?

B Very nice! But he was just as nice to a pack of flame cubs that came by, so maybe he thinks of me like a puppy.

C Sometimes he was nice? But then he'd get mean. Then he'd get nice again. You know what, even if he wanted it to be, I'm deciding that was **NOT** a date.

D I think he **THOUGHT** he was being nice.

How did the encounter end?

A He looked at a clock, said, "Hmm. Interesting," and then left. I found my way out.

B He turned into a flame lion and ran off with the flame cubs. Looked cute though.

C I threw him into a sunbeam and have been ignoring his texts.

D It seemed like he wanted to stay over at the treehouse, but he may have been trying to claim it as an outpost of Lumpy Space, so he could kick us out and make it his royal castle.

RESULTS: Inconclusive.

How about you and ME get out of here. I'm itchin' for some adventure, girl!

HA HA! YEAH!

HOW TO BE MOST BELOVED BY LUMPY SPACE PRINCE

It is very important to be the very best person in the world, and to have others appreciate you for it! Naturally, I cannot teach you how to attain this position, because it is currently held by **ME**. But I may teach you how to rise in your station and become **VERY CLOSE** to Most Beloved.

* Show your royal subjects a life to aspire to! Be a good example of wealth and taste! Be sure to tax them appropriately to budget your aspirational lifestyle.

* Talk trash on others to make the person you are with feel good.

* Take command of situations! But be kind! Treat your servants like your friends, and make your friends be your servants.

* Be handsome. Be very, very handsome. Measure your lumps for ideal shape. Trim your mustache just so. Stretch your eyes out to be **ENORMOUS** and have **IDEAL SPARKLE.**

* If someone is better than you at something, have them display their skill while wearing a suit of purple lumps. Then claim that YOU have done it.

* Have many portraits of you commissioned. Give them out as gifts so people can be reminded of your wonderfulness in their home.

Marshall Lee's SIMPLE RAP BATTLE TECHNIQUE

Oh dang! Marshall's about to take on Rap Bear in a battle
of rhymes! Something seems kind of . . .
formulaic about his technique, though.

I love going out to rap battles and spinning devastating pieces off my vampire dome. But I'll let you in on a secret. It's easier than it looks! All you gotta do to make up some annihilating rhymes is know your schemes and plug in the appropriate diss words! Help me pick the right words to make Rap Bear explode with envy.

To insult you is_____(A)

I make it look _____(A)

With that _____(A from line 2 minus "y" sound)

comes the _____(B)

Watch out, _____(C)

He's about to get _____(C)

He's drowning in rap battle_____(B)

A WORDS:	B WORDS:	C WORDS:
easy	rain	folk
breezy	pain	soak
queasy	Spain	broke
sleazy	train	joke
wheezy	Maine	yolk
sneezy	wane	oak
uneasy	plane	poke
		bloke

SPECTRA'S TIME ROOM

Oh hey, Fionna. Cake. I saw Magic Woman was giving you guys a hard biz, so I thought I'd teleport you out of that situation. Me and Cosmic Robin were just surfing the channels of the multiverse. Which is real? Which isn't? Are you just the dream of one of theirs? Who knows! It's fun to look at.

DREAM INTERPRETATION WITH THE COSMIC ROBIN

Fionna, right? Sorry about that time I showed up in that dream you had where you went to prom, but the limo your date brought turned out to be a bobsled that sent you into a lake of ice. It's not always a fun job being the harbinger of prophetic dreams. **PROPHETIC? THAT NEVER HAPPENED!**

You have to look at the SYMBOLS. Your unconscious mind never likes to tell you things literally. Remember when the Ice Queen disguised herself as Prince Gumball, and tricked you with a crystal sword that was actually a sword of ICE? Your dream predicted it. Think about it. Prom . . . Candy Ball . . . Expectations of your date . . . ruined with surprise ice. Why don't I show you some common symbols, so you'll know what they mean the next time they show up?

DREAM: You're back in high school, and you can't remember where your locker is.
MEANING: You lost twenty bucks. You didn't realize it, and you're never going to find it.

DREAM: A dog is unkind to you.
MEANING: You have done something to upset nature itself. You must right this wrong. Alternatively, you are stressed out about your neighbor's mean dog.

DREAM: You have to build a boat with your uncle, but then your uncle turns into a file cabinet?
MEANING: Your uncle has many hidden memories, and he will only reveal them to you on the briny sea.

DREAM: Your teeth fall out, grow arms and legs, and then put on a three-hour show for you in a tiny theater for teeth.
MEANING: Your mouth wants to sing! Be a performer!

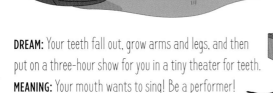

Hey guys, sorry to interrupt, but it looks like there's some total badness happening in the Nightosphere. It could PROBABLY use a hero to stop it. . . .

SEND US!
SEND US!

FINALLY! LET'S BEAT SOMETHING UP!

WELCOME TO THE NIGHTOSPHERE

Aw yeah! Now we're in the ZONE, dude! The more MEGA-EVIL someone is, the more wicked traps and stuff they have in their house! Hana Abadeer is pretty much the only LITERAL QUEEN OF EVIL I know, so this joint is jammed with weird stuff trying to kill us. Here's how to get around them!

ARNING! It's a break om for the DEMONS, t you. Best to move on.

If a random treasure chest is too easy to get to, it's secretly got a mouth that will eat you.

BREAK ROOM

The last two guards you'll have to face before the big boss! Fight them like you fight other things, dude! With punches and kicks!

You need two things here: impeccable timing and crazy good jumping legs. If your legs are only okay, you will lose them.

FINISH

Marshall Lee's BABY PICTURES

Bwa ha ha ha! So nice to have friends of my little Prince of the Nightosphere, Marshall Lee, drop by! He's not here right now, so he can't stop me from showing off his super-evil BABY PICTURES! HA HA HA! —HANA

YEAH WE'RE HERE TO STOP SOME EVIL BADNESS . . .

IS THAT . . .?
So cute! I know!

HA HA, AWW, FAT BABY!

58

I wish he would come back and command my terrible forces again! But all he wants to do is sing and dance in the woods. . . .

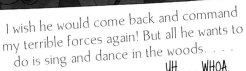

UH . . . WHOA.

AWW! DOES WIDDLE BABY NOT LIKE THE SAND?

Oh, the sun burns him terribly. I hadn't realized that yet. He nearly turned to ash right after this!

Now that's over . . . . I was just about to invade your lands with my demon army! I thought it would be nice to show Marshall what a good army of demons can do! Maybe it'll convince him to come home!

NOT HAPPENING!
BAD MAMA!

AWW, A LITTLE PET.

He ate it after this was taken.

TAKING DOWN THE FINAL BOSS

The bigger they are, the harder I punch their greater surface area!

So, final boss battles are totally my jam! Here's the thing, they always LOOK really tough and intimidating, but they've always got specific strike points you have to look out for. Usually it's some glowing orb or something on their body. Depending on how serious the boss is, you want to prioritize taking out their deadly limbs or weapons.

Don't worry too much about little baddies they spawn. It's a distraction! If you take them out, she'll just produce more!

While you're jumping around, hitting blinky weak points, keep an eye out for patterns. When someone like Hana transforms into a giant monster, that's hard for her to control! It's easier for her to move and attack with specific practiced movements. So like, she swings once with her tentacle, and, if that misses, she pauses for a sec, then goes for a bite in **THIS** general direction. Dodge **THAT** and she's open to attack on her big dumb dorsal zone! **NICE.**

Once you've weakened the boss, be sure to deliver the perfect one-liner before the final blow.

You look **TIRED!**

RELAX AND ENJOY THE
SPOILS OF VICTORY WITH BMO

● ✚ ● ▲ ●

BMO, baby, less talk, more muscle relaxin', please.

I can do both!

It's a pretty wild world of Ooo out there, and it's a great time getting to explore it, but at the end of the day, it's nice to just unwind at home!

You did it! You beat the bad guy! You deserve a break! YAY! With me! BMO!

There are lots of great ways to relax after you have beaten up a demon queen of the underworld!

→ **Have nice food!** Pizza pies are good! So is ice cream! Or healthy salads! Maybe save the salad for tomorrow.

→ **Take a bath!** Put lavender essential oil in it! Don't let me in! I am made of sparky parts!

→ **Get a massage!** Your muscles worked hard! They should get stretched by your robot friend!

→ **Count your treasure!** You have so much treasure! Count it like a mad baron! It's fun!

→ **Identify magic treasure!** Uh-oh! That wand has a skull on it with red jewel eyes! What does it do? Look in a book! It's fun to research your treasure!

→ **Invite friends** over to hear your stories!

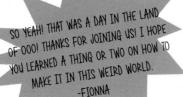

SO YEAH! THAT WAS A DAY IN THE LAND OF OOO! THANKS FOR JOINING US! I HOPE YOU LEARNED A THING OR TWO ON HOW TO MAKE IT IN THIS WEIRD WORLD.
-FIONNA

And if you learned how to stretch yourself into a tire, give me a call, because honestly that's pretty rare, and you might be a freak. Bye!
-Cake

TITAN BOOKS

144 Southwark Street
London SE1 0UP
www.titanbooks.com

Find us on Facebook: www.facebook.com/titanbooks
Follow us on Twitter: @TitanBooks

Published by Titan Books, London, in 2017.

Published by arrangement with Insight Editions,
PO Box 3088, San Rafael, CA 94912, USA. www.insighteditions.com

A CIP catalogue record for this title is available
from the British Library.
ISBN: 9781785655906

Publisher: Raoul Goff
Acquisitions Manager: Robbie Schmidt
Art Director: Chrissy Kwasnik
Designer: Jenelle Wagner
Executive Editor: Vanessa Lopez
Production Editor: Elaine Ou
Associate Editor: Katie DeSandro
Production Managers: Alix Nicholaeff, Thomas Chung and Lina sp Temena
Production Assistant: Jacob Frink

ROOTS of PEACE   REPLANTED PAPER

Insight Editions, in association with Roots of Peace, will plant two trees for each tree used in the manufacturing of this book. Roots of Peace is an internationally renowned humanitarian organization dedicated to eradicating land mines worldwide and converting war-torn lands into productive farms and wildlife habitats. Roots of Peace will plant two million fruit and nut trees in Afghanistan and provide farmers there with the skills and support necessary for sustainable land use.

Manufactured in China by Insight Editions

10 9 8 7 6 5 4 3 2 1

You've Flooped The Pig, are you ready to Floop The Cooper?

Available Now!
www.cryptozoic.com